Specimen Sight-Reading Tests for Saxophone

Grades 1–5

ABRSM

GRADE 1

1

2

3

AB 2470

8 Moderato

9 Lento

rit.

10 Allegretto

11 Andante

rall.

16

17

18

GRADE 2

1

2

3

4 Allegretto

5 Andante

6 Larghetto

10

11

12

GRADE 3

GRADE 4

GRADE 5

AB 2470

Typeset by Musonix
Printed by Caligraving Limited Thetford Norfolk England

11/11